Jesus Is Born!

By SHAUNA GIBBY

Illustrated by CASEY NELSON

DESERET
BOOK

Salt Lake City, Utah

Library of Congress Cataloging-in-Publication Data

(CIP data on file)
ISBN 978-1-62972-469-0

Printed in China
RR Donnelley, Shenzhen, Guangdong, China

5/2018

10 9 8 7 6 5 4 3 2 1

To my babies: Becca, Curtis, Scott, Matthew, and Brian.

I love you bunches!

—SG

To my parents, brothers and sisters, and all of my

nieces and nephews. You help me remember

the meaning of Christmas and truly make it magical.

—CN

To the Hess family —

Have a wonderful Christmas !

♡ Shauna Gibby

People all over the world love the true story of Christmas. Now you can enjoy this story in new ways as you look closely at each page and discover more about the miracle of Jesus's birth.

Shine a flashlight behind the color pages to see what is hidden in each scene.

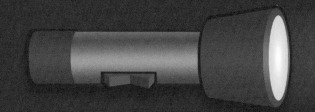

Over 2,000 years ago, a beautiful woman named Mary lived in Judea in a town called Nazareth. She was a righteous woman who loved the Lord.

Who visited Mary?

An angel named Gabriel
came and told Mary that
Heavenly Father favored
her highly and that she
would have a baby.

He would be the Son of God.

Joseph was a **carpenter**, which means he built things with tools. The angel Gabriel also visited Joseph and told him that Mary's baby should be named Jesus.

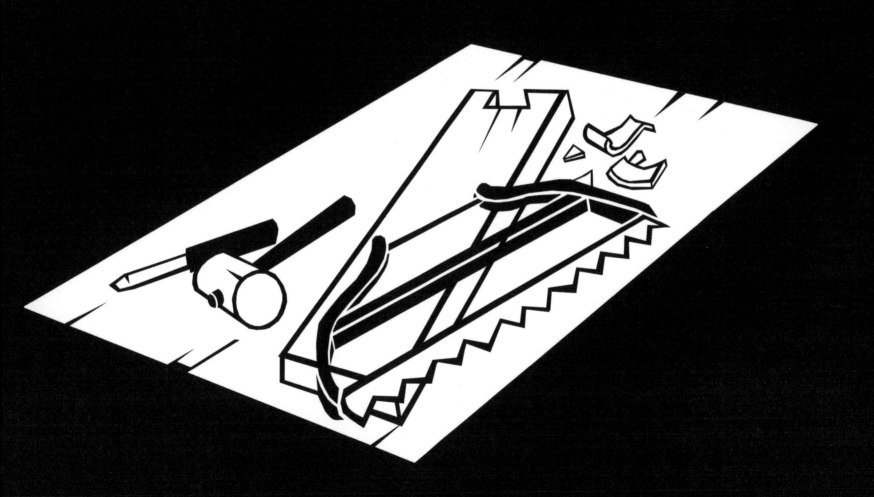

The emperor over all the land told everyone they needed to pay their taxes in the place their family was from. Joseph's ancestors were from a town called Bethlehem.

How would he and Mary get there?

Mary would ride a donkey and Joseph would walk. They had a long way to go.

Mary and Joseph traveled for many days. They had gone more than ninety miles.

Were they almost there?

Yes! They were nearly to
Bethlehem. Mary and Joseph
were very tired, so they were glad
their journey was almost over.

When they got to Bethlehem, Joseph asked
the innkeeper if they could stay at the inn.

What did the innkeeper say?

He told them there was no room.
Many other people had also come
to Bethlehem to pay their taxes.
The inns were already full.

Joseph was worried about Mary—the baby was going to come soon! He found a safe place for her to rest.

Where did they go?

They went to a warm stable
where the animals stay. This
was the only place left in
Bethlehem for them to sleep.

That night Mary gave birth to baby Jesus. She wrapped him in swaddling clothes.

Where did she lay him down to sleep?

Mary laid the baby in a
manger. This is a box
that holds the hay for
the animals to eat.

That night there were shepherds in a field watching their flock of sheep. An angel came and told them the wonderful news that Jesus was born.

What amazing thing happened next?

Lots of **angels** joined him and
they all began to sing! The angels
were so happy that Jesus was born.

They sang, "Glory to God in the
highest, and on earth peace,
good will toward men."

The shepherds hurried to the stable to see the baby.

When they had seen Him and Mary and Joseph, what did they do?

The shepherds wanted to spread
the exciting news that the
Christ child had been born. They
told everyone what they saw. All
who heard them were amazed.

There were some wise men that came from nearby countries. They also wanted to visit the new baby.

How did they know He was born?

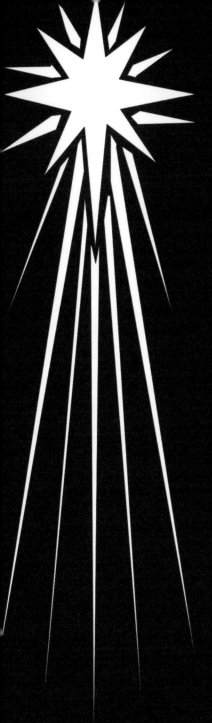

They saw a new star in the sky
and knew it was the sign that the
king of the Jews had been born.
They followed the star to Bethlehem.

The wise men kneeled down and worshipped the baby Jesus. They brought him special gifts.

What did they bring?

The wise men brought treasures of
gold, frankincense, and myrrh.
These were precious gifts fit for a king.

When Jesus was born, another miracle happened on the other side of the world, where the Nephites and Lamanites lived.

How did the people there know of His birth?

There was a day and a night and a day with **no darkness**. The people saw the sun go down, but it stayed light all night long. The next night they also saw the new star. The prophet Samuel the Lamanite had told them that these miracles would happen when the Savior was born.

After the wise men left, Joseph had a dream that baby Jesus was not safe. Joseph knew he needed to take Mary and Jesus to a new land.

Where did they go?

They traveled to Egypt. King Herod of Judea had heard that a baby was born who would become a king. He was angry and commanded that all baby boys be killed. But Jesus was safe in Egypt.

After a while, the king of Judea died. Then Joseph, Mary, and Jesus returned to their home in Nazareth, by the Sea of Galilee. Jesus learned and grew.

What did Jesus do there when he was grown?

Jesus taught many people. He told them to be kind to one another. During his life He taught the gospel and performed many miracles. He died for all people and then was resurrected so we might live again.

We celebrate Christmas to remember the birth of Jesus Christ. He is the light, life, and hope of the world.